pi kids

phoenix international publications, inc.

Life in Arendelle is full of fun! Look around for Princess Anna, Queen Elsa, and their playful pals:

Olaf the snowman dreams about summer days! Can you find these things he would like to try?

Anna and Kristoff like to visit Kristoff's family in Troll Valley. While everyone says hello, look for Grand Pabbie and these other trolls:

Traveling to other kingdoms is a big adventure! As the sisters set sail with Olaf, search for these things they'll need at sea:

Elsa's favorite thing about royal parties is decorating! Find these ice sculptures she's making for the Winter Ball:

The Winter Ball is fun for everyone! Search the party for these pairs of dancers:

The best part of Anna's day is spending time with her sister! While Anna and Elsa hang out in the library, look around for these things:

WHAT'S DIFFERENT?

Nothing makes Olaf happier than summertime fun!
Look for 10 differences between these two scenes.
Check the answer key on the next page!

Hike back to playtime on North Mountain and count these creatures:

1 bunny
2 squirrels
3 birds
4 ladybugs
5 bumblebees
6 butterflies

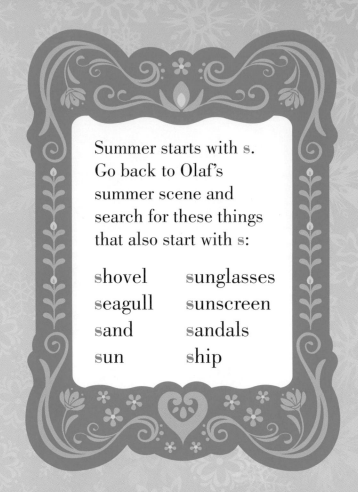

Summer starts with s. Go back to Olaf's summer scene and search for these things that also start with s:

shovel	sunglasses
seagull	sunscreen
sand	sandals
sun	ship

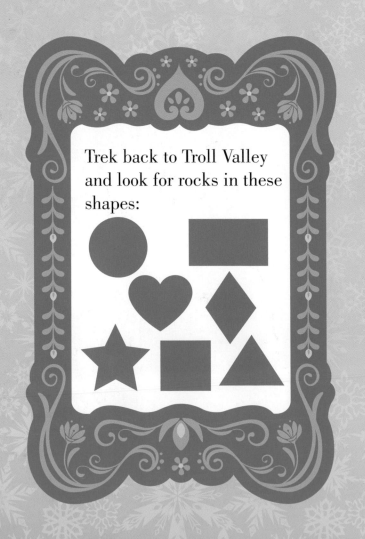

Trek back to Troll Valley and look for rocks in these shapes:

Swim back to the sisters' ship and try to find things that rhyme with these words:

dish (**fish**)
cat (**hat**)
shore (**oar**)
clap (**map**)
hope (**rope**)
pail (**sail**)

Skate back to Elsa's ice sculptures and find these snowflakes:

Waltz back to the Winter Ball and look for these pretty patterns:

Take another trip to the library and find three books of each color:

blue	orange
	purple
green	yellow

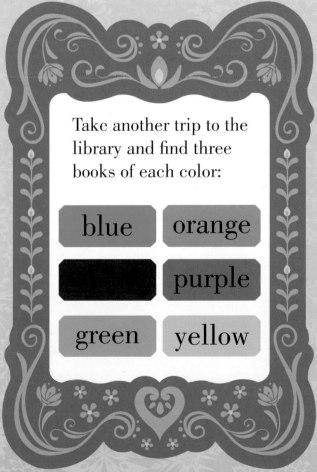

What's Different? Answer Key